CROSBY'S GOLDEN GOAL

MIKE LEONETTI

Illustrations by
GARY MCLAUGHLIN

SCHOLASTIC CANADA LTD.
Toronto New York London Auckland Sydney
Mexico City New Delhi Hong Kong Buenos Aires

A special thank you to the Gremont family for sharing their experiences about attending
the 2010 Winter Olympic Games in Vancouver.

Books written by these authors were consulted: Gare Joyce, Bob McKenzie, Shawna Richer.
Magazines: *Breakout*, *ESPN The Magazine*, *Maclean's*, *Sports Illustrated*, *The Hockey News*.
Record Books: *The NHL Official Guide and Record Book*. Newspapers: *Toronto Star*, *Globe and Mail*.
Websites: NHL.com., wikipedia.com. Video: Outdoor game between Buffalo and Pittsburgh on January 1,
2008 and the gold medal game between Canada and the United States at the 2010 Winter Olympic Games.

Photograph on page 30 © Bruce Bennett / Getty Images.

Scholastic Canada Ltd.
604 King Street West, Toronto, Ontario M5V 1E1, Canada

Scholastic Inc.
557 Broadway, New York, NY 10012, USA

Scholastic Australia Pty Limited
PO Box 579, Gosford, NSW 2250, Australia

Scholastic New Zealand Limited
Private Bag 94407, Botany, Manukau 2163, New Zealand

Scholastic Children's Books
Euston House, 24 Eversholt Street, London NW1 1DB, UK

www.scholastic.ca

Library and Archives Canada Cataloguing in Publication

Leonetti, Mike, 1958-
Crosby's golden goal / by Mike Leonetti ; illustrations
by Gary McLaughlin.

ISBN 978-1-4431-1911-5

I. McLaughlin, Gary II. Title.

PS8573.E58734C76 2012a   jC813'.54   C2012-901654-3

7 6 5 4 3 2   Printed in Malaysia 108   16 17 18 19 20

*To all the kids who play for the fun and love of
the great game of hockey.*
— M.L.

*To the memory of my father, Robert Martin
McLaughlin, and all the hockey dads who
taught their children the "art" of the game.*
— G.M.

"Now boarding flight number 181 to Vancouver," came the announcement at the airport.

"Okay, Tyler, that's us," Dad said as we went toward the gate.

The 2010 Winter Olympics were being held in Vancouver, and I was so excited to be going. Dad had gotten tickets for some of the hockey games, including the medal rounds and the gold-medal game. I was hoping Team Canada would win, and I could not wait to see my favourite player, Sidney Crosby, wearing the red maple leaf.

It was a long flight, and I had a *Sports Illustrated* magazine to read. The cover had a photo of Crosby with the caption "Sidney's Moment." It made me think about my year away from hockey.

I had been a pretty good player on my Triple A team, but it seemed like I was playing hockey all the time. Games and practices, power skating, summer hockey, off-ice workouts, going to the outdoor rink near home — it seemed like there just wasn't time for anything else.

Sometimes I wanted to play other sports, hang out with my friends and play video games. I lost track of how many things I had to miss because of hockey.

After our final game last season, I made up my mind. I knew it wasn't going to be easy to tell my dad.

"Dad, you know how you always said it was my choice to play hockey? Well, I've decided that I don't want to play next year," I said.

"What?" Dad said. "Why, Tyler? You're doing so well."

"It's not fun any more," I said.

"But you loved to play from the moment you first stepped on the ice with a stick. What if you change your mind? You might not ever catch up to everyone else."

"Maybe. But I want to do other things for a while," I said.

"Okay, Tyler," my dad sighed. "It's your choice."

The guys couldn't believe that I was going to quit hockey. My winger and best friend Jake tried to talk me out of it. "You'll feel different in September when the season starts again," he said. But my mind was made up.

Jake still dropped over to watch hockey on TV like we did before, and sometimes I would go to the outdoor rink and shoot the puck around with Dad. I played in the driveway, but other than that I stayed away from hockey.

It was actually nice to spend more time with my family — even my little sister Maddy!

As we were about to land in Vancouver, I looked down at my magazine again. The whole country would be watching, hoping Canada could win the gold medal. The team was loaded with young stars like Jonathan Toews, Corey Perry and Drew Doughty. They also had good veterans like Scott Niedermayer, Joe Thornton and Jarome Iginla, and Martin Brodeur and Roberto Luongo in net.

But the star of the team was Crosby, and all eyes would be on him.

I loved the way Crosby played. He always wanted the puck, and he would move quickly to take a shot or make a crisp pass. He wasn't the biggest player in the league, but he had great heart and a desire to be the best player in the NHL.

I remembered watching him when he first joined the NHL — the first year I really followed hockey. His rookie season, when he was only 18, he recorded 102 points. The next year he had 120 — the most of any player in the league. By the end of his fourth year, he was captain of the Penguins and they were Stanley Cup champions. His goals could bring the fans out of their seats.

One of the highlights of my life was going to the very first Winter Classic game in Buffalo. It was snowing, but there were more than 70,000 people in the outdoor stadium.

It came down to a shootout with Crosby up against Sabres goalie Ryan Miller. Miller tried to stop Sid with a poke check, but Crosby put the puck right between Miller's pads for the winning goal. A big smile came over Crosby's face and you could see how much he loved the game!

But the Olympics were even more exciting. Team Canada beat Norway 8–0 and Crosby scored the shootout winner against Switzerland. But then Team USA handed Canada a 5–3 loss, and the Canadians had to fight back and win the next three before making it into the gold-medal game against the Americans.

Our tickets were in the first row of the upper balcony. We saw Gordie Howe and the prime minister! Canadian flags were waving everywhere.

Team Canada scored the first two goals of the game on shots by Toews and Perry, but Team USA would not quit. They had great players too, like Zach Parise, Patrick Kane and Phil Kessel, and Miller in net. Going into the third period it was 2–1 for Canada and the action was fast.

Then, with just 25 seconds to go, Parise managed to get free in front of Luongo to tie the game! I couldn't believe it. The game would go to overtime — four-on-four hockey for 20 minutes, and then, if it was still tied, to a shootout.

Team Canada came out strong in overtime, but Miller made save after save. But I remembered Crosby beating Miller in Buffalo, and I knew he could do it again. Then, about seven minutes into the overtime, Crosby came out with Iginla. Crosby took a pass from Niedermayer and tried to rush straight up the ice, but the defencemen pushed him back. The puck slid along the boards and Crosby chased it, chipping it over to Iginla. He spun toward the USA net and yelled out, "Iggy, Iggy!" Iginla put a pass right on Sid's stick.

Crosby shot the puck all in one motion. Miller looked like he was going to try the poke check, but the puck went right through his pads. Crosby had scored the golden goal!

Dad and I hugged and we started high-fiving everyone around us.

The players came over the boards to mob Crosby, who had tossed his equipment in the air and had a huge smile on his face. The crowd roared when Sid got his gold medal and when he took a large Canadian flag for a skate around the ice. It was a moment I'll never forget.

I tried to sleep on the flight home but I just couldn't. The excitement of the game had me thinking about everything I loved about hockey, and watching Crosby score and then celebrate with his teammates made me realize how much I really missed being on a team.

Dad looked over at me. "Wasn't that great, Tyler?"

"The best. It could not have been any better . . . well, maybe if I could score a goal like that someday."

"I guess you'll have to start playing hockey again, then," Dad said with a grin on his face.

I just smiled.

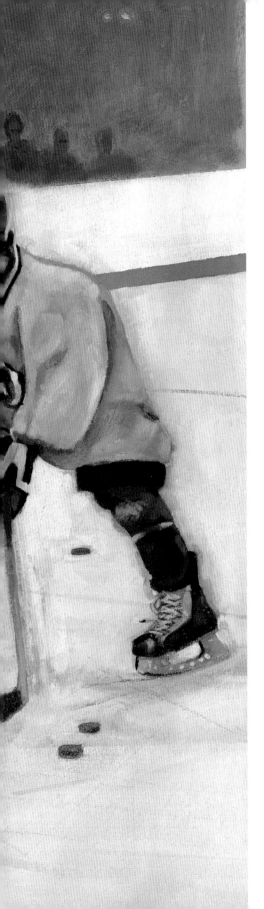

After we got home, I went to see the coach of the Lions. I asked him if I could go to the tryouts in April, and he said I needed to be serious about it. "Show me the passion is back, Tyler," Coach Lowes said as he looked me straight in the eyes.

"I'll be ready, Coach. I want to compete again."

My mom and dad were happy to hear about my decision. "This time we're not going to make it all about hockey. We're going to balance things out more," Mom said.

"Let's focus on getting better every game and having fun," Dad added.

It sounded good to me.

I worked hard to get ready for the tryouts, and Jake and a few other guys helped me to prepare. I felt fresh and strong on the ice. I made the team, and soon I was back playing on a line with Jake.

We really started to click again by the time we got to our first tournament. We won three out of four games, and I scored three times. The Lions made it to the final. We were tied late in the game when I sprung Jake with a long pass.

Jake fired a hard drive on net, but the goalie gave up a huge rebound and I shot it right away. It went in and my teammates were all over me. It turned out to be the winning goal!

It felt so good to be back playing. I thought a lot about Crosby and how much he loved to play the game. I still had a poster in my room of Sidney holding his minor hockey sweater. It said, "My first goal was having fun." I looked at that poster every day. Most of all I remembered how much fun Sid the Kid still seemed to be having, and how he had brought me back to hockey.

ABOUT SIDNEY CROSBY

Sidney "Sid the Kid" Crosby was born on August 7, 1987, in
Cole Harbour, Nova Scotia, where he began playing minor hockey.
He quickly showed that he was going to be a dominant player. He
played major junior hockey with the Rimouski Oceanic of the QMJHL,
beginning in the 2003–04 season. In his final year with Rimouski, he
scored 66 goals and totalled 168 points, making him the most sought-
after prospect in hockey. The Pittsburgh Penguins drafted him first
overall in 2005 and he immediately became the superstar everyone
expected. He scored 39 goals in his rookie season, totalling 102 points.
The following season he won the Art Ross Trophy with 120 points, as
well as the Hart Memorial Trophy as the most valuable player in the
NHL. He was named captain of the Penguins in 2007, and his team won
the Stanley Cup in the 2008–09 season.

Crosby had 66 points in 41 games during the 2010–11 season
but missed the second half of the year after suffering a concussion.
He returned to action on November 21, 2011, scoring twice and adding
two assists in a 5–0 Pittsburgh win. After that game he said, "The main
thing was just the joy of playing and that is something I've missed for
the last 10 months." He was reinjured but eventually returned to play
in a total of 22 regular season games in 2011–12, recording 37 points.
He added another eight points in six playoff games. Crosby is considered to be the face of the National
Hockey League.

TEAM CANADA AND INTERNATIONAL HOCKEY

Sidney Crosby's goal at the 2010 Winter Olympics wasn't the first dramatic goal scored for Team Canada.
In 1972, when Team Canada played an eight-game series against the Soviet Union in what was called "The
Summit Series," Paul Henderson scored the winner for Canada with just 34 seconds to play in the last
game. It is still considered the greatest goal ever scored by a Canadian player in international hockey.

In the first Canada Cup tournament in 1976, Darryl Sittler scored the tournament-winning goal for
Team Canada when they beat Czechoslovakia in overtime. And 11 years later, Mario Lemieux scored
after taking a pass from Wayne Gretzky to give Canada a 6–5 win in the third and final game of the 1987
Canada Cup between Canada and Russia.